CW00548958

MS FINNMARKEN
Hurtigruten AS

Kaptein / Captain

MS FINNMARKEN

Kjøkkensjef / Head chef

MS FINNMARKEN

Hotellsjef / Hotel Manager

Pål Brekke & Fredrik Broms

NORTHERN LIGHTS

— A GUIDE —

0 9 FEB 2017

Crossed the arctic circle
MS FINNMARKEN

Pål Brekke & Fredrik Broms

NORTHERN LIGHTS

— A GUIDE —

press

CONTENTS

NORTHERN LIGHTS — A GUIDE

ACKNOWLEDGEMENTS

We would like to thank Professor Truls-Lynne Hansen, Professor Asgeir Brekke and Dr. Magnar G. Johnsen for valuable discussions and suggestions regarding the historical and physical section of the book.

FREDRIK: I wish to extend my deepest gratitude to my grandfather Gösta Carlsson. Without him this book would not have been realised. By teaching me the names of the stars and introducing me to the books of Fridtjof Nansen, he inspired me to study science in the high Arctic, where the seed of this book was planted. Although I lost my guide much too early, he will always be with me under the northern lights and keep inspiring me. Most of all, I wish to thank Lotta Borg for her endless love and support and for all the magic moments under the northern lights together. Most of the photos in this book would not exist without her help and encouragement. Finally I wish to thank Nicole Baeten for always being there as my sister and for keeping my head above water and my parents for their great support during the preparation of this book.

PÅL: I would like to thank previous colleagues at the University of Oslo and at NASA Goddard Space Flight Centre for inspiring me to spend time presenting science for the public. The entire Norwegian space science community has also been very helpful throughout the years whenever I needed information and help. All this knowledge has now been condensed into this book and they all have a share in it. I am also thankful for having a very patient family around me when I am deep into my space thoughts or on one of numerous travels around the world.

CHAPTER ONE

Hunting the Northern Lights – An Introduction

INTRODUCTION

The northern lights have fascinated people throughout history and few natural phenomena on Earth are able to inspire a stronger sense of wonder in us than the majestic dance of the auroras. While a pair of binoculars or even a telescope may be required to fully appreciate the magnificence of many other astronomical phenomena, the northern lights are there for everyone and require no other optical aids than your own eyes.

In "Northern Lights – A Guide" we cover all aspects of auroras; from how our understanding of auroras has evolved from myth to modern science, how we can predict and forecast when and where strong northern lights are likely to occur, and provide practical information about the best strategies to observe and record auroras. The book is presented in a way so that the reader can quickly go to the section that interests him most without having to delve deeply into the preceeding chapters. The book can therefore be used either as a complete introduction to northern lights which can be read from cover to cover, or as a field guide where the reader can switch easily between different sections.

No understanding of the physical processes that cause the auroras to occur is needed to appreciate their beauty. However, knowing more about the processes that cause the sky to shimmer with bright curtains adds another dimension to the experience. By explaining, in lay language, the processes that cause the northern lights, we hope that this guide will prove an ideal companion for anyone who wishes to learn more about auroras.

Hunting for the northern lights is a bit like hunting for mushrooms – the more time you spend outside looking, and by looking at the right places at the right times of the year, the more likely you are to find them. In "Northern Lights – A Guide", we will reveal our best "mushroom places" and our best recipes for a successful hunt. We will start off by introducing some of the best places to see the northern lights and some start-off tips to consider for anyone who wishes to incorporate aurora watching in their future plans.

WHERE TO TRAVEL?

If you are travelling north in quest of the auroras, your best option will be to travel to the area around the aurora zone - a ring-shaped band where the chances of seeing the northern lights are highest. The aurora zone stretches across the northern part of Scandinavia (Norway, Sweden, and Finland), over to Siberia in northern Russia, and then across Alaska and the northernmost parts of Canada, and further across southern Greenland and Iceland. It is in these places that you have the best chances of seeing auroras, and the best time period to go is between mid September and mid March.

Just as there is an aurora zone in the north, there is also an aurora zone centred on the southern pole, where southern lights may be seen. However, the southern aurora zone largely spans inaccessible parts of the Antarctic Ocean and southern lights can therefore only be seen in more populated areas during strong auroral activity when the extent of the aurora oval is expanding. Under such conditions, auroras may be seen from the southernmost parts of Australia and New Zealand as well as from the southern tip of South America, but since this only happens rarely the focus of this book will be on the northern aurora zone.

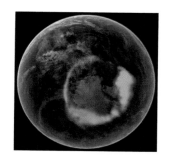

The southern aurora zone stretches over remote areas of the Antarctic Ocean and is therefore difficult to access for an aurora hunter. (NASA)

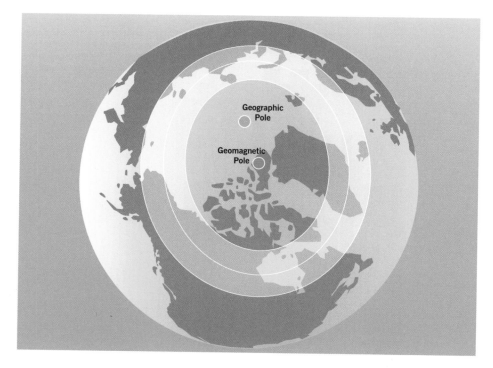

Northern lights are most commonly seen under the aurora zone
– a circular belt that is centered on the geomagnetic north pole.

PRACTICAL CONSIDERATIONS – LOCALITY AND WEATHER

In addition to the geographical locality, the chances of seeing auroras depend largely on the current solar activity and on the weather situation here on the Earth. While auroras can be seen to some degree on almost every clear night within the aurora zone, the largest and most spectacular auroras appear only during increased solar activity, even at high latitudes. Your best strategy is to contact tour operators in the area that you plan to visit to learn more about the best time to go.

One of the most important factors to consider is the weather. Since the auroras are located at a height of approximately 80 to 250 km above the Earth, and even the very highest of clouds reach only 5-10 km up, you need a clear sky if you want to see auroras, wherever you go.

The weather is, of course, notoriously unpredictable, but generally speaking it varies considerably from one part of the aurora zone to another. It also varies by season, so it is well worth checking the weather statistics for the time of the year in the area that you plan to visit. Most inland areas have a more stable climate than coastal areas but may be more difficult to reach. While offering excellent aurora-watching possibilities, large areas of the aurora zone, such as the vast expanses

The local weather conditions may change rapidly.
The photo to the right was taken only 30 minutes after the photo to the left.

of Siberia, Canada, and Greenland, are comparably inaccessible to the traveller. Winter temperatures in the majority of inland areas in the aurora zone can also test the endurance of most people; throughout almost the entire zone, temperatures below -10°C, or even below -30°C, can be common on clear nights. Many prefer the milder climates in, for example, the coastal areas of the Nordic countries, notably Norway and Iceland, where, thanks to the Gulf Stream, the climate is milder than it is in other locations at the same latitudes. These areas are also much easier to access and are therefore excellent destinations for the aurora watcher but can, in comparison with many inland areas, try your patience with what may sometimes feel like perpetual rain or snowfall if you are unlucky. Some of the places that are most famous for their excellent aurora-watching possibilities include Tromsø in northern Norway, which is known for its accessibility, relatively mild climate, and reliable auroras (because it is located more or less directly under the aurora oval). Other well-known aurora-watching sites include Abisko in northern Sweden, Rovaniemi in northern Finland, Fairbanks in Alaska, and most of Iceland. The more inaccessible areas in Canada, Russia, and Greenland also offer aurora tours under especially dark and pristine skies.

Tromsø in Northern Norway is located directly underneath the aurora oval and is a popular aurora watching site.

The Polarlightcenter in Laukvik, Norway combines high knowledge about the northern lights with a cozy atmosphere.

JOINING AN ORGANIZED TOUR – OR NOT?

Aurora-watching can take many different forms. Whether you decide to go aurora-hunting on your own or decide to join an organized aurora-watching trip is, of course, completely up to you. It might be nice to try to do both.

Organized tours fall into three main categories: land-based trips, aurora-watching boat trips, and specially designed flights that will take you under the aurora oval so that you can look at the auroras from an airplane. Land-based trips are naturally very popular and allow participants to combine aurora-watching with other activities, such as dog-sledding, skiing, kick-sledding, and trekking, as well as making trips to special destinations by car or snowmobile. In Iceland, it is also common to combine aurora-watching with, for example, horseback riding. In general, tour operators are very familiar with the areas in which they work and can offer expert advice about the best times to visit. Many will do all they can to find a place for you where the sky is clear. Some can also provide equipment, warm winter clothes, and information about auroras generally as well as about local history. There are a vast number of different ways to experience the auroras, each offering something different. A few dedicated operators, such as the Polarlightcenter in Lofoten in Norway, have even built their own magnetometers and other measuring devices so that they can provide custom-

The northbound Hurtigruten M/S Kong Harald leaves the port in Tromsø on its way along the Norwegian coastline.

The coastal steamer Hurtigruten sails under dark skies in the aurora zone in Northern Norway.

ers with aurora alerts by text message as soon as the auroras start. Perhaps the best-known way of observing auroras at sea is by booking passage on Hurtigruten, the coastal steamer that sails along the entire Norwegian coastline. In northern Norway, the ship not only passes below the aurora zone under dark skies but also provides scenic views of the majestic coastline and rugged fjords and mountains. In several places, moreover, you can find smaller boat operators and arrange tailor-made trips on sailing ships. Special "aurora flights" that take you under the aurora zone by air-plane are available in some areas, such as Britain.

Wherever you decide to go and whatever kind of plans you decide to make, it is strongly recommended that you take the time that the experience is worth and make arrangements that allow you to enjoy the magic of the northern lights. If you travel north in search of the auroras, we strongly advise you to spend not just one or two nights in the area, but to stay for several days and nights in order to make it less likely that your plans will be spoiled by bad weather (space weather as well as local) and also in order to be able to explore places of local interest. Before you set out, it is recommended that you contact the local tourist information office, which will be able to tell you what kind of aurora-watching trips are available as well as to provide more general tourist information.

Renting a car to go aurora watching is popular and gives you a lot of freedom and flexibility.

POLAR DARKNESS – A LIGHT YOU WILL NEVER FORGET

To get good weather and a good aurora display at the same time can be a challenge, but if you spend some time in the aurora zone your chances of experiencing something truly spectacular are high. Clear skies are never guaranteed, of course, no matter where you go, but it is not only the northern lights that make the high northern sky so special, and even if auroras do not turn up, the distinctive Arctic light is truly enchanting in and of itself.

All areas north of the Arctic Circle experience what is known as "polar darkness" or "polar night" during part of the winter. When it is polar night, the sun does not rise above the horizon. In the same areas, for a part of the summertime, the sun never sets. This is known as the "midnight sun". The length of the polar night depends on the latitude. While polar night at the Arctic Circle lasts for only about 20 hours, areas north of the Arctic Circle experience much longer periods without sun. In Tromsø in northern Norway, for example, the polar night last from the end of November to the end of January; at the North Pole it lasts for 179 days of the year! While the sun does not rise, the sky is far from pitch black in most areas around the aurora zone, and the characteristic beautiful blue light of twilight can be seen during most of the day. In areas well inside the Arctic Circle, a long slow dawn in hues of pink and blue seems to herald the rising of the sun, but just when you think the sun is about to rise, the long slow dusk begins. Already in the afternoon, the brightest stars start to come out. Many people travel to northern areas just to experience this special light, and in most areas north of the Arctic Circle the "return of the sun-day" is a big event that is celebrated and often people climb mountain peaks to get a first view of the sun before it returns to ground level.

In the high north, this is the time when everyone seems to want to meet a friend over coffee or hot chocolate in a café or to light candles and sit and talk in front of a fire and enjoy the silence. The northern winter is also the time when the ice on the surface of lakes and of the sea sings its mysterious ice songs and owls call from the wintry forests. With some luck, auroras can be seen dancing across the sky by the early afternoon, and for much of the polar night period the snow lights up the landscape in the north, which is far from dark. It is a truly magical time and well worth experiencing.

CHAPTER TWO

———

From Myth to Science – Understanding the Northern Lights

———

For thousands of years, people in the northern part of the world have marvelled at the spectacular displays that occasionally light up the night sky. This stunning phenomenon is deeply embedded in the mythology of many cultures, and in the past the northern lights were said to be caused by everything from dancing spirits to God's anger. But no one suspected a connection with the sun. The first to propose a connection with the sun were the French scientist Jean-Jacques d'Ortous de Mairan and the Norwegian scientist Kristian Birkeland.

After decades of research, we now know that auroras appear when charged particles from the sun interact with the Earth's magnetic field, which directs the particles into the atmosphere at polar latitudes. Here they collide with gases and create the light display we call the northern lights. Monitoring the activity of the sun, then, can make it possible, to some extent, to forecast the strength and location of the aurora.

MYTHS AND SUPERSTITIONS

Most northern cultures have a wide variety of oral legends about the aurora which have been passed down from generation to generation. During the Viking period, northern lights were described as reflections of dead maidens or as reflections of the shields of the Valkyries, female warriors who chose which slain warriors should be escorted to Valhalla – the hall, ruled by the god Odin, in which the slain spent their afterlife. Ancient texts from which the known legends stem are often difficult to interpret and it can therefore be difficult to know for certain how ancient cultures have reacted to auroras. But it is known that the phenomenon was often referred to as a vengeful being. In ancient times, most people were afraid of the lights. Some people would not let their children outside to play while there were auroras, fearful they could get killed. Others thought it was all right as long as the children wore hats so that the aurora would not burn their hair off. In both Scandinavia and North America, some people believed that one could summon the aurora by whistling, but that to do so could be dangerous.

Many cultures also believed that the aurora was a place for the dead, in particular for people who had died a violent or too early death, people who had been murdered, who had taken their own lives, who had been killed in war, or who had died in childbirth. Other cultures believed that it was a message from the Creator. An old tale from the Nordic countries said that "God is angry when the aurora flames." In other cultures it was considered an omen of impending war, disaster, or plague.

The Inuit people in Greenland believed that the northern lights represented the souls of stillborn children who were playing ball with a walrus skull or with their

The Inuit people in Greenland believed that the northern lights represented the souls of stillborn children who were playing ball with a walrus skull. (I. Sandahl)

Explorer Leiv Eriksson painted by Christian Krogh in 1893.

afterbirth. The Mandan Indians of North Dakota explained the northern lights as fires over which the great medicine men and warriors of northern nations simmered their dead enemies in enormous pots. One romantic conception found in Danish folklore is that these lights were caused by a throng of swans who had flown so far to the north that they had been caught in the ice. Each time they flapped their wings, they created reflections, which resulted in the northern lights. In Norway, children were often told that if they waved their hands with white clothes, the motion of the aurora would increase the more intensely they waved. In Russia, the northern lights were associated with "Ognenniy Zmey" – the fire dragon. The dragon seduced women when their husbands were out. In Scotland, and in the Shetland and Orkney islands, the auroras were known as "the mirrie dancers" or "na fir-chlis", which means the nimble or lively ones. The dance often ended in a fight and was often considered a prediction of bad weather.

As will be discussed later, when the northern lights extend to lower latitudes they typically take on a reddish hue. Often people thought that large areas to the north were on fire. In AD 37, the Emperor Tiberius observed a very red sky north of Rome. He immediately thought that the town of Ostia had been attacked and set aflame and sent his army to protect those living there. The same kinds of thoughts have struck people throughout history, and even as late as 1938, when a major aurora display with a red hue could be seen over central Europe, a fire brigade was summoned to Windsor Castle in England to put out a fire that turned out to be auroras.

The many names

The northern lights have been given a number of names throughout history. It was the Vikings who christened the northern lights "norðurljós". The Finnish name for the northern lights, "revontulet", is associated with the Arctic fox. According to a folk tale, an Arctic fox is running far in the north and stirring up snow with its tail, thus causing ice crystals to fly off into the sky. Those crystals are the northern lights. The Sami people called it "guovssahas", meaning "the light you can hear". Many people still claim that they can hear the northern lights. (We will return to this topic later.) The scientific name for the phenomena is "aurora borealis", which is Latin and translates as "dawn of the north". Its counterpart is "aurora australis", or southern lights. It was the Italian scientist Galileo Galilei (1564-1642) who first used the expression (actually he said "borealis aurora"). When the aurora is extremely active it moves farther south, as will be explained later. On the latitude at which Galileo was living, northern lights are mainly red in colour. The French astronomer Pierre Gassendi used this expression after a

According to a Danish folklore these lights were caused by a throng of swans that had been caught in the ice. When they flapped their wings it created reflections seen as northern lights.
(I. Sandahl)

OPPOSITE PAGE
From southern latitudes the aurora often appears as a red glow on the northern horizon, ominously suggesting a great fire.

Emperor Tiberius was once tricked by a very red sky north of Rome.

major aurora outbreak on 12 September 1621 and turned Galilei's expression around into "aurora borealis".

The aurora borealis has since been the international name for the northern lights, while its counterpart in the southern hemisphere is called aurora australis. Interestingly, in the 1730s the Swedish scientist Anders Celsius argued against the name aurora borealis and suggested another Latin name, luminis borealis or "the northern lights". He was supported by many other Scandinavian writers. His suggestion was very close to the original name, norðurljós, given to the aurora by the Vikings.

Galileo Galilei was the first human to point a telescope towards the night sky. (Sarah K. Bolton/Justus Sustermans)

The Finnish name for the northern lights, "revontulet", is associated with the Arctic fox. (E. Karvanen)

EARLY SCIENCE

The first realistic description of auroras is probably found in the Norwegian chronicle which dates to about AD 1230. It was originally written as a textbook, probably for the sons of King Magnus Lagabøte. At that time people thought the Earth was flat and surrounded by oceans. One explanation was that the oceans were surrounded by fire and that auroras were the light from those fires reflected in the sky. Another possibility was that reflected sunlight from below the horizon illuminated the sky. A third explanation was reflections from glaciers.

In more modern times, the Swedish scientist Suno Arnelius (1681-1740) published his thesis in 1708 suggesting that the aurora represented solar rays reflecting off ice particles in the atmosphere. Rene Descartes proposed a similar theory. The Norwegian priest Jonas Ramus (1649-1718) argued that the aurora could not be reflected sunlight and distanced himself from the ideas put forward in and by Arnelius.

A particularly strong aurora on March 6, 1716 could be observed in large parts of Europe and gave birth to more modern science. Many people in Europe thought it was a new natural phenomenon, since it had not been observed at those latitudes for a long time. Sir Edmond Halley published the first detailed description of the aurora in that year. He lamented that at the age of 60 years he had given up all hope of experiencing this amazing phenomenon. He suggested that "auroral rays are due to

The Norwegian chronicle The King's Mirror from AD 1230 gave several realistic explanations of the northern lights.

Sir Edmond Halley,
English astronomer best known for computing the orbit for comet Halley.

King Magnus Lagabøte,
Norwegian king between 1263 and 1280. (P. Byhring)

the particles, which are affected by the magnetic field; the rays are parallel to Earth's magnetic field." Furthermore, he argued that the top of the arc of the aurora did not point toward the geographic pole but rather toward the magnetic pole.

Joachim F. Ramus was the first Norwegian to write a scientific paper on the aurora, in 1745. The Swedish scientist Anders Celsius (1701-1744), best known for his temperature scale, and his co-worker Olof P. Hiorter found a correlation between the occurrence of the northern lights and variations of the compass needle. Similar findings were presented by George Graham (1673-1751) from England. He concluded that the aurora was a global phenomenon. In 1868 Anders Jonas Ångström, also from Sweden, used a prism to show that auroral light differs from sunlight, suggesting that the auroras could not be caused by reflections from other light sources.

The Norwegian astronomer Christopher Hansteen (1784-1873) established several observing stations and arranged with sea captains to observe and record the magnetic field all over the world. Hence he became the first to point out that the aurora occurs as a continuous ring around the geomagnetic pole. Sophus Tromholt (1851–1896) from Denmark organized a network of northern lights observation stations. He also pointed out that the northern lights seemed to form a luminous ring around the North Pole. Hansteen's and Tromholt's drawings are the first illustrations of what was later to be known as the auroral oval. Tromholt also showed that auroral occurrences correlate well with the 11-year sunspot cycle.

Illustration by Christopher Hansteen showing the aurora as a continuous ring around the polar region. (C. Hansteen)

KRISTIAN BIRKELAND – A BREAKTHROUGH IN THE UNDERSTANDING OF THE NORTHERN LIGHTS

A major breakthrough was made by the Norwegian scientist Kristian Birkeland (1867-1917), who proposed that charged particles from the sun could ignite auroras. To prove his theory, he built a simple model of the solar system that consisted of a small model of the Earth (called terrella) with an electromagnet inside that was suspended in a vacuum chamber. With the help of the electromagnet, he was able to establish a magnetic field around the terrella that resembled the Earth's magnetic field. The atmosphere was a layer of fluorescent paint that emitted light when struck by charged particles. He demonstrated how particles injected into the glass box could ignite luminous rings around each of the poles. The particles were captured by his model planet's magnetic field and channeled down toward the Polar Regions.

Birkeland also established the first permanent aurora observatory. In addition, he demonstrated the existence of the solar wind. Based on his geomagnetic surveys, which showed that auroral activity was nearly uninterrupted, he concluded that the Earth was being continually bombarded by "rays of electric corpuscles

The Norwegian 200 kroner bill shows Birkeland, with his Terella experiment, the Big Dipper, the pole star, and the aurora oval. (Norges Bank)

emitted by the sun." Birkeland also studied the properties of comet tails. Many of his ideas were not confirmed until the Space Age, some 60 years later.

Two other noteworthy Norwegian researchers in this area were Lars Vegard, the first scientist to map the colours of the aurora, and Carl Størmer, who picked up where Birkeland had left off and calculated that there is a belt-like area around the Earth in which particles are reflected back and forth between the poles. Verification of the existence of this region came years later as a result of satellite measurements made by the American physicist James van Allen. Today these particle belts are called the van Allen belts.

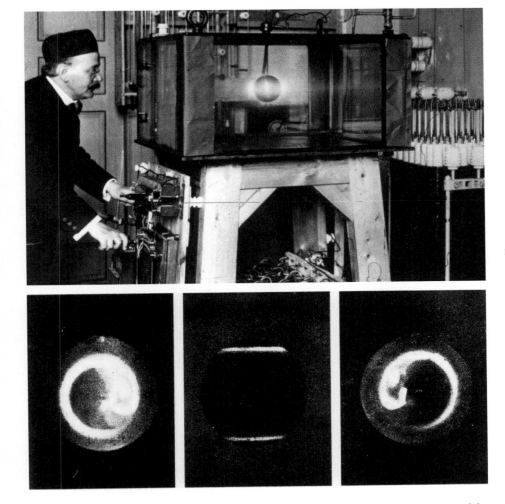

LEFT
Kristian Birkeland with his Terella experiment,
a vacuum chamber in which a small magnetized
metal sphere (a stand-in for Earth) is bombarded
by electrons injected into the box.
(University of Oslo)

The particles were captured by Birkelands model planet's magnetic field and channeled down toward the sphere's polar regions, where they ignited aurora-like glows. (University of Oslo)

The height of the northern lights was a controversial subject for a long time. Some suggested that they extended down to a few kilometers above the ground while others suggested that the distance from the ground was closer to 800 km. By taking large numbers of pictures of the northern lights simultaneously from two different locations, Størmer calculated the height of the aurora more accurately, finding it to be somewhere between 80 and 130 km. Today we know that it typically extends from about 80 to 250 km and on rare occasions up to 500 to 800 km. The aurora, then, is not a weather phenomenon, since almost all weather occurs in the first 16 km of the atmosphere.

Carl Størmer with his aurora camera.
(University of Oslo)

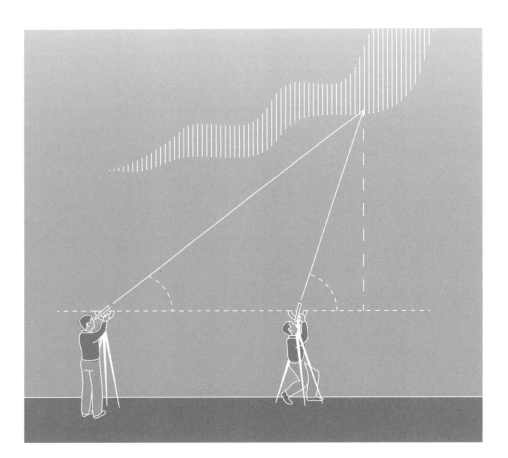

By taking simultaneous images of the same northern light structures from two different locations, Størmer could calculate the height of the aurora.

Auroral sound – a myth?

There are many stories about people claiming that strong auroras often are accompanied by sound. Many people still argue that they can hear some crackling sounds – often synchronized with the movements of the aurora. The aurora occurs at heights above 80 km where the atmosphere is nearly a vacuum. Since sound waves cannot propagate when air pressure is so low it should be impossible for sound to travel down to the ground.

An interesting explanation was put forward during Roald Amundsen's expedition to the South Pole in 1911. One of his expedition members, Hjalmar Johansen, noted in his diary that Roald Amundsen, after being outside, told his companions he could hear his breath freezing in the air when exhaling. Johansen and his colleague Prestrud went outside and they, too, could hear this crackling sound – a sound that they remembered having heard at Svalbard during strong aurorae. When they stopped breathing or moved their heads in a different direction, however, the sound ceased.

The question of whether the aurora emits a sound is still debated today. Recently a group of Finnish scientists claimed to have found the answer to this mystery. Using three microphones during high auroral activity to triangulate the source of the sounds, they concluded that the sounds are emitted much closer to the ground from the same solar particles from which the aurora is generated. They are still not sure which mechanisms are involved, since there are many types of sounds, which suggests that various mechanisms may be at work. Hence the name "guovssahas", used by the Sami people, seems to be valid.

Roald Amundsen's Expedition reaching the
South Pole in 1911.

LEFT
Could the claimed "aurora sound" just be
the freezing of water vapor?

The northern lights in art and music

The aurora has been a source of inspiration for many painters, writers, and composers. Expeditions to the Arctic often resulted in beautiful artworks, such as the famous prints made by the Norwegian explorer Fridtjof Nansen. Many painters have since created very beautiful and realistic paintings and lithographs of auroras. To be lucky enough to see the aurora is indeed a beautiful experience. In 1883, a well-known Norwegian author, Theodor Caspari, concluded a poem with the following line: "You are to me, Aurora, a symbol of life."

A quick search on the Internet will lead you to hundreds of albums or songs related to the aurora or northern lights. Every February there is, for example, a week-long Northern Light Festival in Tromsø in northern Norway, featuring everything from popular science lectures to jazz concerts and art displays. And what can be better, after a concert about the aurora, than to step out into the winter night and perhaps experience the northern lights right then and there?

Willy Stoffregen, who worked as an engineer at The Aurora Observatory in Tromsø in the 1930s, set music to Theodor Caspari's poem "Northern Lights".

Wooden carving by the Norwegian explorer Fridtjof Nansen.

MODERN SCIENCE

After decades of research involving ground-based observatories, sounding rockets, and satellites, we now know that auroras appear when charged particles from the sun interact with the Earth's magnetic field, which directs the particles into the atmosphere where they collide with gases and emit the light that we call auroras. By monitoring the activity of the sun, therefore, one can forecast the strength and location of the aurora.

A large number of other all-sky cameras and other scientific instruments are situated in many northern countries to study the northern lights. The EIS-CAT project consists of a series of antennas (incoherent scatter radars) in northern Scandinavia and Svalbard to study the interaction between the sun and Earth. Three of these large antennas are located at the Ramfjordmoen facility outside Tromsø, Norway; in Sodankylä, Finland; and in Kiruna, Sweden. In addition, there are two large EISCAT antennas at Svalbard. The new Kjell Henriksen Observatory is also located at Svalbard and is the largest of its kind in the Polar Regions. It was opened in 2008 and contains 30 instrument rooms, each with a glass dome. Here, scientists around the world can remotely operate their instru-

The large EISCAT antennas at Svalbard with the northern lights as a backdrop. (N. Gulbrandsen)

A two-stage Black Brant rocket arced through an aurora 230 kilometers above Alaska to investigate the underlying physics of the northern lights. (L. Wingfield/NASA)

ments from their home institutions. What makes Svalbard special is that it is located directly below a weakness in the Earth's magnetic field where particles from the solar wind can enter directly into Earth's atmosphere and create the daytime aurora.

Using rockets launched from Fairbanks, Alaska, and Andøya or Svalbard in Norway, one can spear through the aurora and actually measure its physical properties. Satellites provide a global view and have provided a great deal of new knowledge about the northern lights and the interaction among the solar wind, the magnetosphere, and the atmosphere (e.g. Polar, Cluster and THEMIS).

Today we have a quite good understanding of the natural mechanisms that create the northern lights. As often in science, especially when it becomes possible to make more accurate observations, new discoveries have raised a number of new questions. So it is that we still need to improve our knowledge about the sun-Earth connection.

The laser beams from the ALOMAR observatory at Andøya explore Earth's atmosphere.
(K. Dahle/ARR)

CHAPTER THREE

Causes of
the Northern Lights

For us humans, the sun, as seen with the naked eye, appears as a static and quiet yellow sphere in the sky. But it is, in fact, a stormy and variable star and contributes much more than just light and heat to our planet. It is the source of the northern lights and can affect our technology-based society and climate on Earth. To understand the northern lights we need to understand the sun and its interaction with Earth's magnetic field and atmosphere.

THE STRUCTURE OF THE SUN

The sun contains over 99% of the mass of the solar system, and about 1.3 million Earth-sized objects could fit inside it. The sun is made of gas, mostly hydrogen and helium. Just like the Earth, the sun is constantly rotating. One rotation takes about 27 days. This was first noticed and described by Galileo, who studied the sun with his telescope in 1610. He noticed that sunspots moved each day from east to west on the solar disk as the sun rotated.

The core of the sun

The hot compact core of the sun – where its energy is created – has a radius of about 175,000 km. The temperature is over 15 million °C, and enormous pressure pushes the atoms very close together, causing them to collide with each other constantly. The collisions convert hydrogen nuclei to helium nuclei and, as a result of this process, some of the mass is converted to light or photons. This energy keeps the sun shining after the energy has pushed itself through the interior of the sun to its surface. The processes in the core also create particles called neutrinos. About 700 million tons of hydrogen are converted into helium every second, and about 4 million tons of mass are converted into neutrinos and into radiation in the form of gamma rays.

The sun's energy production per second is an incredible 3.86×10^{26} watts, or 386 billion billion megawatts. This is more energy than Norway, at its present level of electricity consumption, would consume in 600 million years.

OPPOSITE PAGE
To most people the sun appears as a quiet bright sphere moving across the sky each day. This photo shows the sun as seen during the historical transit of Venus on 6 June 2012. In addition to the planet Venus, several sunspots can be seen on the solar disc. Stø, Vesterålen in Northern Norway.

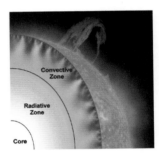

The structure of the sun: the inner core, the radiation zone, and the convection zone. (NASA)

The surface of the sun – the photosphere

The part of the sun that we actually can see from the Earth with the naked eye is called the photosphere. This is the part of the sun from which most of its energy is radiated. Although the photosphere is not a solid surface but a 400-km-thick layer of gas and part of the sun's atmosphere, this layer is commonly called the sun's surface. The photosphere, which has a temperature of about 5,000 °C, is covered by a cell-like pattern called granulation, whereby hot gas bubbles up from deeper layers, cools down at the surface, and sinks down again in thin, darker lanes. This is not unlike what can be observed on the surface of a simmering pot of soup.

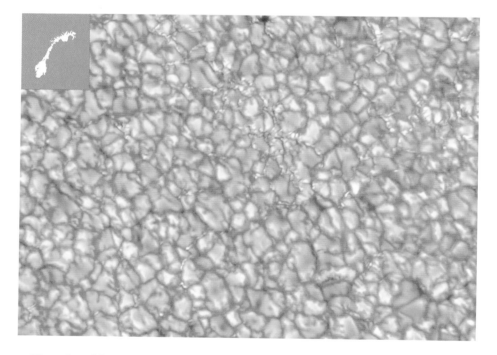

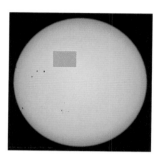

The surface of the sun as seen in visible light. (SDO/NASA)

The surface of the sun consists of a mottled pattern we call granulation. Each cell is on the average 1,800 km across, or about the length of Norway. The area on the sun is marked in the full disk image to the right. (Hinode/NAOJ)

Sunspots

The most visible features on the solar surface are dark areas called sunspots. Sunspots occur when a strong magnetic field formed in the solar interior pushes itself out through the surface. The strong magnetic field will prevent some of the upwelling energy from reaching the surface in these regions. This makes them somewhat cooler and this cooler gas will then appear darker. The magnetic field in large sunspots can be 10,000 times stronger than Earth's magnetic field.

Sunspots can be very large, as much as 50,000 km in diameter, which means that they are dozens of times the size of the Earth. When the sun is low on the horizon and the sky is hazy, it is possible to glimpse large sunspots with the naked eye. You should never look at the sun, however, without using proper protection for your eyes.

The sun in visible light with some large sunspots.

The sun's atmosphere – the chromosphere

Just above the photosphere, we find the lower solar atmosphere, called the chromosphere. This pinkish layer of gas extends 3,000 km out from the photosphere and can only be observed during a total solar eclipse or by using special telescopes, preferably in space. Chromosphere means "colour sphere" and is hotter than the surface of the sun. At the outer part of the chromosphere, the temperature reaches 30,000 to 70,000 °C, compared to the 5,000 °C photosphere. The chromosphere mainly emits ultraviolet radiation, which is blocked by the Earth's atmosphere and thus cannot be studied in detail from the ground.

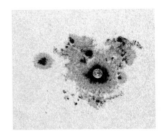

Close-up of a sunspot observed with NASA's TRACE satellite. Earth fits well inside the spot. (TRACE/Lockheed)

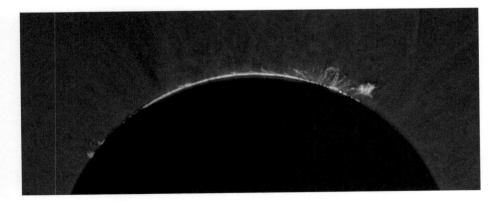

The chromosphere seen during a total eclipse. Large flamelike prominences rise up in the corona. (M. Druckmuller)

Prominences

Prominences are composed of chromospheric gas. They are suspended in the outer solar atmosphere by strong magnetic fields and can be seen as bright structures above the solar limb, sometimes reaching a height of 50,000 km. When these same structures are seen against the solar disk, they look dark, since they absorb the bright light from the surface. Then they are called filaments. Sometimes prominences and filaments can erupt and eject gas out into space. Such events are called coronal mass ejections or CMEs for short. If one such cloud of gas encounters Earth's magnetic field, we experience strong auroras.

The outer solar atmosphere – the corona

Just outside the chromosphere the temperature starts to increase very rapidly and we find the outer solar atmosphere – the corona.

The density of the corona is very thin and consists mostly of hydrogen gas. Strangely, the temperature of the corona is between 1 and 2 million °C. Owing to its very low density, the corona emits very little light. It is therefore impossible to see it every day because of the strong light from the photosphere and the scattered light in the Earth's atmosphere. Only during rare total solar eclipses, when the moon passes in front of the sun and blocks the strong light from the photosphere, can we see the spectacular corona with the naked eye. By inserting a small occulting disk inside a telescope that blocks the bright light from the solar disk, we can create artificial eclipses and make it possible to study the corona in great detail on a daily basis, and thus observe eruptions on the sun that could result in strong northern lights.

The extremely high temperature of the corona is one of the sun's biggest mysteries. The energy from the solar interior must in some unknown way be able to pass through the relatively cold photosphere and chromosphere without heating these layers. The energy is then deposited in the corona and heats it to several million degrees. An analogue could be a light bulb. The temperature of the filament is very high, while the surrounding glass has a much lower temperature (though it is still quite hot to touch). If the air outside the glass were higher than the glass itself, you would wonder how the energy from the filament could heat it up without heating the glass.

The sun manages this in some strange way. We still do not yet fully understand this mystery, but it probably involves energy stored in the sun's magnetic fields. It may also involve sound waves that travel out through the atmosphere and deposit the energy up in the corona.

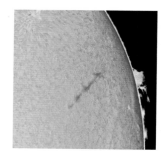

Prominences are bright features suspended in the hot corona. When prominences are observed against the bright solar disk they look dark and are called filaments. (W. Higgins)

OPPOSITE PAGE
By observing the sun with instruments that only detect ultraviolet lights one can observe the very structured hot corona. (SDO/NASA)

OBSERVING THE SUN FROM GROUND AND SPACE

Modern ground-based solar telescopes are often built on top of mountains where it is clearer and where there is less disturbance in the atmosphere, providing sharper images of the sun. The most recent are built on islands with tall mountains such as Hawaii, Tenerife and La Palma. Here telescopes are located above the clouds most of the time and can study the sun most days.

The sun emits both visible and "invisible" light. This includes ultraviolet light (UV) and X-rays. It is mainly the visible light that penetrates the atmosphere and reaches Earth's surface. UV and X-rays are absorbed by Earth's atmosphere and to observe this part of the solar emission we need to be in space.

The Swedish telescope at LaPalma, Canary Island is one of the best in the world. (Swedish Academy of Sciences)

The first satellite-based solar telescopes were launched in the early 1960s. More recent satellites like the Solar and Heliospheric Observatory (SOHO) have revolutionised our knowledge about the sun. SOHO was launched December 2, 1995, and was placed 1.5 million km from Earth (four times the distance to the moon), between Earth and the sun. From this vantage point we call Lagrangian point number 1 (L1), SOHO can study the sun day and night. Situated outside the magnetosphere it can also measure the speed and density of the solar wind. It is an important tool for space weather and aurora forecasting. SOHO includes a special telescope called a coronagraph. The Large Angle Spectrometric Coronagraph (LASCO) takes images of the solar corona by blocking the light coming directly from the sun itself with an occulter disk inside the telescope, creating an artificial eclipse within the instrument. It is the perfect tool for detecting CMEs, in particular those heading toward the Earth. To a certain degree scientists can use these observations to estimate the arrival time of a CME. Thus, one can indicate possible upcoming strong auroras 1-3 days in advance.

Solar and Heliospheric Observatory was launched in 1995 and monitors the sun 24 hours every day. (NASA)

Another important satellite orbiting L1 is NASA's Advanced Composition Explorer (ACE). It provides important measurements of the solar wind and CMEs. About one hour before the solar wind or a CME hits the magnetosphere it will pass ACE, which then can measure the density and speed of the passing gas. In addition ACE can measure the orientation of the magnetic field embedded in the solar wind or the CME. This is a very important measurement and will determine how severe the geomagnetic storm will be. The measurements from ACE give us a one-hour advanced forecast of the northern lights.

Since 2006 NASA's two STEREO satellites have provided us with an additional view of the sun and CMEs. STEREO consists of two space-based observatories – one ahead of Earth in its orbit, the other trailing behind. Currently they view the sun and the Earth from the "side" and provide images of CMEs while they are travelling from the sun and pass the Earth. These observations are very useful to estimate the arrival time at Earth.

In 2010 NASA launched the Solar Dynamics Observatory (SDO). The satellite takes images with four times higher resolution than HD TV and pictures every 10 seconds in each wavelength it observes. It transmits impressive 1500 Gbyte of data every day and monitors the activity on the sun in detail. Real-time images from SOHO and SDO are available for the public on the Internet.

THE SOLAR CYCLE

The sun undergoes variations on many time scales, but the best known is the 11-year cycle. Every 11 years or so, the sun passes through a period we call "solar maximum", during which there are many large sunspots, strong magnetic fields, and many solar storms. About five years later, the sun enters "solar minimum", a period during which there are few or no spots and few solar storms. By recording the number of sunspots at various times, we can follow the pulse of the sun and the way in which the magnetic forces and the number of solar storms are changing. We have a good record of sunspots since 1610, when Galileo first used his telescope. The total energy output from the sun also varies with the solar cycle, with the sun emitting 0.1% more energy than usual during solar maximum.

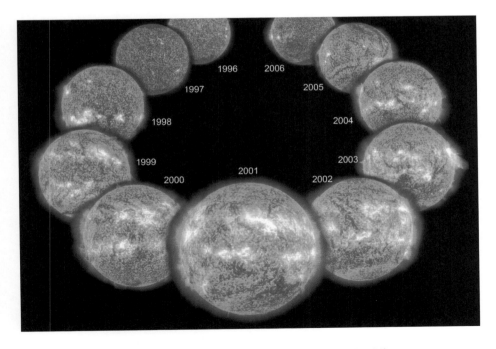

The activity on the sun varies in an 11-year cycle. (ESA/NASA)

Solar storms

Solar storms are caused by intense releases of energy on the surface of the sun. There are basically three different types of events:

- Large explosions in the solar atmosphere, called "flares", are caused by unstable magnetic fields that release in mere seconds an amount of energy corresponding to several billion megatons of TNT. Large amounts of UV radiation and X-rays travelling at the speed of light are emitted and the radiation strikes the Earth's atmosphere 8 minutes and 20 seconds later. Fortunately, this radiation is blocked by our atmosphere and does not reach the ground.

- CMEs occur when large amounts of gas and magnetic fields are ejected from the sun's atmosphere out into space. They expand in space and can reach velocities up to 8 million km/h. Even at this speed, it would take almost 20 hours for a CME to reach the Earth.

- On rare occasions, CMEs and flares can accelerate large numbers of high-energy particles – so-called proton events. Consisting mostly of protons, these particles have such high speed and energy that they can penetrate satellites and spacecrafts.

Of these events it is CMEs that are causing strong northern lights at lower latitudes if they are heading towards the Earth. When the CME reaches the Earth, the particles are deflected by our magnetosphere. The clouds of gas push and shake the Earth's magnetic field and generate a kind of "storm" that we call a geomagnetic storm.

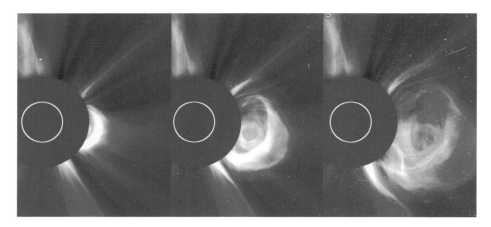

A coronal mass ejection (weighing a billion tons of gas) is launched out into space. The images were taken by the LASCO instrument on SOHO. A small disk inside the telescope blocks the bright light from the solar disk, creating an artificial eclipse. (SOHO/ESA/NASA)

THE SOLAR WIND AND THE MAGNETOSPHERE

In addition to light the sun sends out a continuous stream of charged particles that we call the solar wind. This stream mainly consists of electrons and protons. The solar wind blows out into the solar system at a typical speed of about 400 km/s or 1.5 million km/h. A flight from Oslo to New York would take only 15 seconds at this speed! The solar wind speed is not constant. Coronal holes are regions in the solar corona where the sun's magnetic field stretches out in space. These regions allow the solar wind to escape with speeds up to 3 million km/s. Thus, coronal holes create strong gusts.

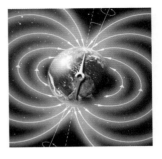

The Earth acts like an enormous bar-magnet
and the magnetic field extends far out in space.
(P. Reid)

Luckily for us, the Earth has a protective magnetic field around itself. Our Earth is an enormous magnet and Earth's magnetic field extends far out in space where it is shaped by the solar wind. We call this area the magnetosphere. This is where Earth's magnetic field dominates over the solar wind. Without it Earth's atmosphere would slowly be blown away from our planet and there would not be any life left here. The magnetosphere is compressed by the solar wind on the solar side (or day side) and is stretched out in a very long tail on the night side.

The sun's magnetic field isn't confined to the immediate vicinity of our star. The solar wind carries it throughout the solar system. We call the sun's extended magnetic field the Interplanetary Magnetic Field (IMF). Because the sun rotates (one revolution every 27 days), the IMF has a spiral shape – named the "Parker spiral" after Eugene Parker, the scientist who first described it.

The solar wind is "blowing" out into space
and pushing on Earth's magnetic field.
(NASA)

The Earth's magnetic field points north where the magnetosphere meets the solar wind. If the IMF points north when it pass the magnetosphere, there will be little interaction with Earth's magnetic field. But if the IMF points south – that is, opposite to Earth's magnetic field – the two fields link up.

In this case we usually say that the solar wind or an incoming CME is "geo-effective" and it will create a stronger disturbance in the magnetosphere. This will furthermore lead to strong northern lights and expand and push the ring-formed bands also known as the auroral oval farther south.

INDICES OF AURORAL ACTIVITY

Since the activity of auroras is directly connected with the solar wind speed, the direction of the IMF or the solar storm activity, knowing something about the processes that cause the auroras is of great help to be able to determine the optimal times for viewing the most active aurora displays. By understanding and checking the most commonly used indices given on aurora forecasting sites (see Useful Internet Resources) will help you to maximise your chances of seeing a spectacular aurora display and allow you to be prepared in advance.

Geomagnetic storms are major disturbances in the magnetosphere. They are caused by solar wind gusts, negative IMF or a CME which interacts with the magnetosphere. The frequency of geomagnetic storms increases and decreases with the sunspot cycle. CME-driven geomagnetic storms are more common during high solar activity while storms driven by high solar wind speeds (from coronal holes) are more common during solar minimum.

We can monitor geomagnetic storms using sensitive instruments called magnetometers. A large number of magnetometers are distributed around the world and provide local measurements of Earth's magnetic field at ground level. A magnetometer is kind of a sophisticated compass. During a geomagnetic storm a compass needle will actually move slightly and can deviate a few degrees from its

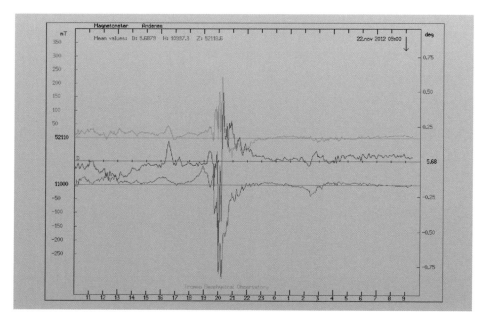

Using a magnetometer one can monitor variations in Earth's magnetic field. Large fluctuations mean there are northern lights overhead. (TGO/UiT)

normal position. In principle you should not trust a compass during a severe geo-magnetic storm if you are located at high latitudes.

Measurements from a grid of many magnetometers are compiled in real time by e.g. NOAA's Space Weather Prediction Center in the USA and converted into 3-hourly global geomagnetic index. It is derived from the maximum fluctuation in the horizontal magnetic field components observed on a magnetometer related to a quiet day and is called the Kp index. The Kp index is therefore used as a global geomagnetic storm index with a scale from 0 to 9, with 0 being quiet conditions and 9 severe storm activity.

Based on the Kp index, you can immediately know if there is a chance of see-ing the aurora. Several web sites are also deriving a "real-time" Kp index based on the latest solar wind observations from ACE. This provides a one-hour advanced forecast of the possibilities to see the aurora. In addition you can check real-time magnetometer observations online from a measuring station close to where you are located. If you are in Norway you can find several stations distributed along the country and when there are large fluctuations in the magnetic field there should be aurora overhead. There are also other geomagnetic indices like Aa, DST etc. that all serve as a guide to determine if the aurora can be seen from your location.

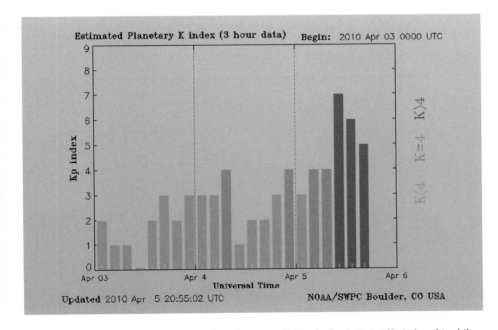

The variation of the Kp index over a few days. Active conditions (yellow) start at Kp index of 4, while storm conditions (red) start at Kp index 5. (NOAA)

The maps on page 61 show the locations where, on average, the aurora oval will be overhead at midnight for different values of Kp. As can be seen, even for a Kp index of 0 and 1 the aurora is visible in the far north of Scandinavia and Alaska. The higher the Kp index climbs, the closer the aurora oval moves towards the equator. Active conditions starts at a Kp index of 4, minor storming at Kp index 5 and major storms starts from Kp index 6.

As can be seen from the maps, at a Kp index greater than 4, auroral activity can be visible in southern Norway and in the upper states in the USA. If the Kp index approaches 9 the aurora can be visible all the way down in southern Europe and the southern states in the USA. In extreme cases the aurora can be seen almost anywhere on Earth. In February 1872, for example, the northern lights were seen in Bombay and in Egypt, and in September 1909 they were observed in Singapore and Jakarta! More recently, in July 2000, they were seen as far south as in Florida.

The primary oval zone passes over northern Scandinavia, the northern part of Iceland, through northern Canada, through northern Alaska and the northern coast of Siberia. From the map, it is quite obvious that the far northern part of Norway is one of the best places to experience the northern lights, both due to the ease of access compared to many other places at a similar latitude and also because of the fairly mild winter climate. It is often called the "Gentle Country of the northern lights" due to the fairly mild winter climate.

A useful satellite observation to keep an eye on is the auroral activity observed from NOAA's Polar-orbiting Operational Environmental Satellite (POES). The satellite is monitoring the power carried by the electrons and protons that produce the aurora and these "images" will give an estimate of the current position of the aurora oval.

The location of the aurora oval for different levels of the Kp index.

The lower circle indicates how far south you can be and still see the northern lights on the horizon.

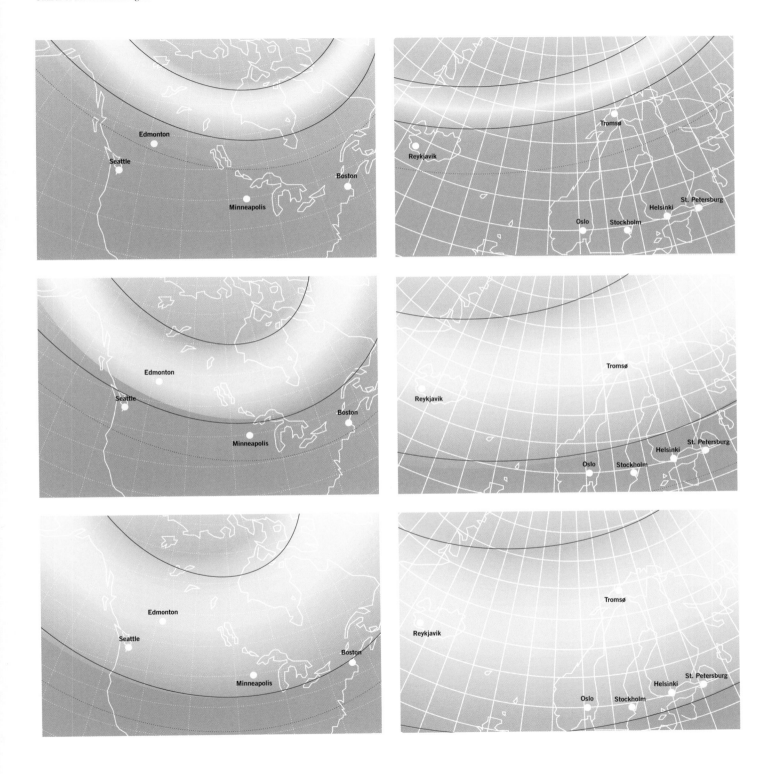

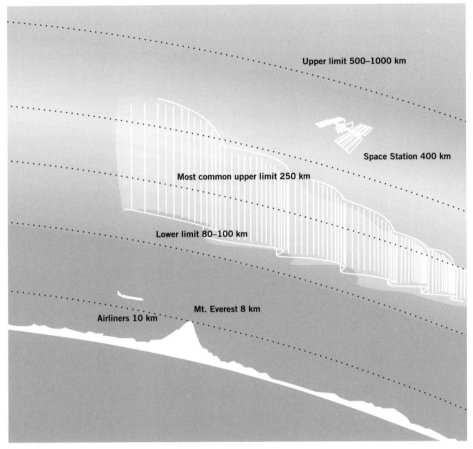

Upper limit 500–1000 km

Space Station 400 km

Most common upper limit 250 km

Lower limit 80–100 km

Mt. Everest 8 km

Airliners 10 km

The height of the aurora compared with the typical height of clouds, the highest mountain peak on Earth, Mount Everest, the typical cruising altitude of an airliner, and the space station.

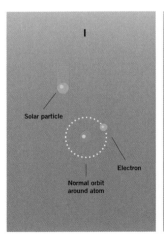
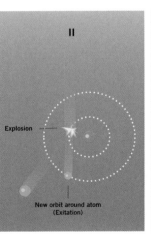
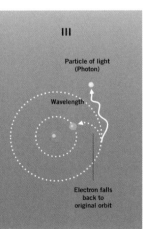

Particles from the sun collide with atoms in the atmosphere, exciting them so that electrons are lifted up into higher orbits. The electrons will quickly "fall back" to their original orbits and release energy in the form of light.

THE COLOURS OF THE NORTHERN LIGHTS

The aurora is formed when particles from the sun, either from the solar wind or CMEs, interfere with our magnetosphere. This process can be explained in simplified fashion by saying that some solar particles manage to penetrate the magnetosphere on the night side (tail). When solar storms cause a disturbance, the magnetosphere particles inside this magnetic cocoon are ejected back towards the Earth along the magnetic field lines. The particles are guided by the magnetic fields down towards the Polar Regions. When they reach the Earth's atmosphere, they collide with oxygen and nitrogen atoms and molecules. These collisions, which typically occur at altitudes between 80 to 250 km, transfer some energy to these atoms, which immediately send out light of a certain frequency and colour.

Atoms consist of a nucleus and of several electrons which encircle the nucleus in distinct orbits. When charged particles strike atoms in the Earth's atmosphere, some of the energy is transferred to the atoms, causing electrons to move to higher-energy orbits farther away from the nucleus. In such situations, the atom is described as being in an excited state. Quickly, the electron jumps back to a lower-energy orbit and releases this energy as a photon – that is, in the form of light.

Oxygen atoms are the cause of the two most prominent colours of the aurora – green and red. The brightest colour in the aurora is green or yellowish-green. Nitro-

At high altitudes the red emission from excited oxygen atoms dominates the colour of the auroras and appears in the upper part of the green rayed bands in the photo.

gen molecules produce bluish light and deep red. The highest part of the auroral curtain is usually red, since red oxygen emission occurs at high altitudes. The middle is greenish-white, while the lower edge is purple. Another kind of purple aurora can sometimes be seen early in dawn, just before sunrise, as the sunlight is falling on ionized nitrogen molecules in the high atmosphere and causing an intensified emission of light.

The collisions result in a spectacular glowing atmosphere, with green, red, white, and blue colours. The mechanism is very similar to what happens in a commercial neon-lit sign, in fluorescent lamps, or on an old-fashioned TV set.

The northern lights can display a variety of shapes and structures. The most common is the curtain-shaped structures that move and flicker. They are a visible manifestation of the way in which the sun shakes up the magnetic field of the Earth. One can observe dramatic shifts that disappear and quickly return — all under the control of the buffeting solar wind. (We will discuss different types of aurora in more detail in Chapter 4.)

POLAR LIGHTS ON OTHER PLANETS

Polar lights are not exclusive for the Earth. In fact they can be observed on many other planets such as Jupiter, Saturn, Uranus, and Neptune. These planets all have an atmosphere and magnetic fields. Thus, polar lights on these planets are caused by the same mechanism. The solar wind and eruptions on the sun are causing disturbances in their magnetic fields and directing particles into the polar regions of their atmosphere, which then glow as giant neon tubes. Observed from satellites, we can see that the polar lights on the planets are very similar to those on Earth.

Polar lights observed on Saturn by the Hubble Space Telescope. (NASA)

EFFECTS ON LIFE ON THE EARTH

The auroras never hurt a sailor or a farmer. It is only with our modern electricity-based societies, and electronic and space technologies, that the storms from the sun can become damaging. The more we do in space, and the more we depend on modern electronics, the more serious and potentially costly the problems of a severe solar storm will become. Today, more than one thousand satellites are operating in space. Our modern society depends to a very high degree on having these satellites working properly all the time. If solar storms damage satellites, many systems on which we depend in our daily life, such as GPS navigation systems, can be disrupted. Solar storms can even be a hazard to astronauts due to high-energy particels from the sun.

Long-term variations in the energy output from the sun can also affect the Earth's climate. Historical temperature records often display variations in sync with variations in solar activity. During the last 100 years, human activity, such as the emission of greenhouse gases, land-use changes, and deforestation, has also contributed dramatically to climate change. If we want to understand human-caused climate change, we also need to better understand natural changes in climate. This requires a better understanding of the connection between solar activity and the effects it has on the Earth.

Variations in solar activity can contribute to climate change. Here a "sunset" is seen from the Space Shuttle. (NASA)

Our modern society depends heavily on technologies that are vulnerable to geomagnetic storms and severe space weather events may knock out power grids, which can have huge consequences.

CHAPTER FOUR

—

Observing
the Northern Lights

—

Watching the northern lights or "aurora borealis" dancing overhead on a clear winter night is one of the most spectacular and awe-inspiring sights that the natural world can offer. They differ from all other light phenomena by exhibiting an amazing variety of colours, structures, and movements. Few people who have caught a glimpse of the northern lights once are left untouched; the sight often leaves memories that last a lifetime.

Briefly put, the possibility of seeing auroras depends mainly on 1) your location and the time of the year and 2) the current geomagnetic activity. The weather situation at the your location and other factors such as interfering light from cities (light pollution) and the darkness of the sky also play an important role.

WHERE AND WHEN TO SEE THE NORTHERN LIGHTS

The aurora zone

The locations where the chance of seeing auroras is greatest are those that are close to the so-called which are oval-shaped regions located around the geomagnetic poles of the Earth. Here, particles from the sun are accelerated along the magnetic field lines, causing the auroras to appear. Auroras can therefore be seen more or less permanently around the aurora ovals. Because the solar wind is pressing upon and shaping the magnetosphere, the aurora oval is broader on the night side of the Earth. Whereas the positions of the aurora ovals are more or less stationary in space, the Earth is rotating beneath them, and because of this daily rotation, the aurora ovals "touch" a circular band of the Earth. For practical reasons, it is easier to talk about these circular bands, or, rather than the ovals, and the aurora zones will be the term that will be mostly used henceforth.

There is one aurora zone located around the north magnetic pole (where the aurora borealis may be seen) and one aurora zone around the south magnetic pole (where the aurora australis occurs). Since the southern aurora zone covers extremely remote areas of the Antarctic Ocean, where few people set foot, the focus of this book will be on the northern aurora zone, but the same information applies to the southern lights. A common assumption that figures largely in the literature is that the auroras in each hemisphere are virtual mirror images of each other. This notion can be traced in large part to observations made from two jet planes that flew simultaneously over the two hemispheres in 1967. Recent satellite observations of the aurora, however, have shown that auroras in the two hemispheres can also be totally asymmetric.

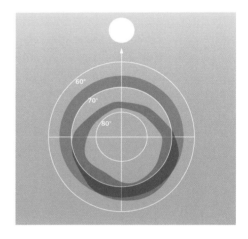

The aurora oval (green) is the belt around the geomagnetic north pole where aurora activity is highest. The belt is displaced toward Earth's night side, especially during increased auroral activity. The circular region (purple) traced out by the maximum equatorwards extent of the oval is known as the aurora zone and is the region where you have the best chance of seeing auroras.

In the northern hemisphere, the aurora zone is centred more or less on the 65° N latitude, coinciding roughly with the Arctic Circle. The width of the band depends largely on the strength of the auroral activity, but is generally only around 10° wide. This means that the aurora zone typically covers the land masses of northern Scandinavia (Norway, Sweden, Finland), northern Russia, Alaska, northern Canada, southern Greenland, and Iceland. It is in these areas that the chance of seeing auroras is best.

The best time to see the northern lights

Within the aurora zone, the northern lights are present both day and night all year round, but during the daytime and in the summer months, it is too bright outside to be able to observe them. No matter where you are, it needs to be dark for you to be able to see auroras. The strongest aurora displays often occur between 8 p.m. and 2 a.m. local time in Europe and between midnight and 4 a.m. in North America in the period from mid September to mid March, but strong auroras may also be seen in August and April. From mid April to mid August, it is too bright to observe auroras in the northern hemisphere.

It is a common belief that it has to be cold for auroras to be seen. While there is no connection between aurora activity and temperature, the sky tends to be clearer on a cold night than on a warm night, and as a consequence the chances of seeing the northern lights increase. Accordingly, the weather in the location from which you plan to observe auroras is therefore an important consideration. In much of the Arctic and sub-Arctic, the skies tend to be clearer in the late winter and early spring than in the autumn.

For reasons that are still not fully understood, particularly strong auroras tend to occur during the months around the equinoxes – that is, early autumn and spring – and that time period (September/October and February/March) is therefore one of the best times to see auroras. Part of the explanation for this involves the sun's magnetic field near the Earth (IMF) and the tilt of the Earth's spin axis. As seen from the sun, the Earth's tilted axis seems to wobble slowly back and forth over a one-year period. This wobbling motion is what makes the IMF wax and wane in sync with the seasons. For an aurora observer who is following aurora forecasts and indices as described in chapter 3, the take-home message here is that if the tilt of the IMF is south-pointing (i.e. south-pointing B_z), the solar wind can reach the inner magnetosphere of the Earth and allow the solar wind to reach the atmosphere directly. This means that if you see a south-pointing B_z figuring in space weather forecasts, strong auroras are likely to grace the skies. This is more often the case in the spring and autumn.

Geomagnetic activity

Although your chances of seeing auroras on a regular basis are better the closer you are to the aurora zone, it is possible to observe auroras from almost anywhere on our planet depending on the solar activity. The solar activity waxes and wanes according to an 11-year cycle, known as the solar cycle, and generally speaking it is during the years around the solar maximum that auroras may be seen more frequently in areas where they are otherwise only rarely observed. On a shorter time scale, strong energy releases on the sun cause disturbances of the Earth's magnetic field every now and then, causing the aurora ovals to expand down to lower latitudes. The expansion is mostly pronounced on the night side of the Earth. During such disturbances, the oval is enlarged and auroras may occasionally be seen as far south as the temperate latitudes. If you monitor auroras it will usually be possible to predict the nights on which auroras will be most likely to be observable at your latitude.

Even less intense auroras may be seen south of the aurora zone owing to the height of the auroras. Most auroras occur between 80 and 250 km above the ground; in comparison, a normal jet aircraft flies at an altitude of approximately 10 km and thus well below the lower part of the auroras. The fact that the height of the auroras is so great means that it is possible to observe them well south of the aurora zone, and even relatively moderate auroras may be seen as far south as several 100 kilometres from the aurora zone.

Because of the great height of auroras, it is possible to see auroras from areas south of the aurora oval. The typical view is then a green arc or band stretching from east to west on the northern horizon.

DIFFERENT TYPES AND STRUCTURES OF THE NORTHERN LIGHTS

Auroras can take on many different forms and colours, and their appearance may change rapidly. Many different basic structures may be recognised, and depending on the intensity of the auroras and your location and perspective, they may be more or less easily distinguishable. Most of the different structures are variations of two major types: and auroras, the former including most of the structures that we normally think of when we think of auroras, for example fairly well-defined and bright structures, whereas the latter type is less well-defined and less distinguishable. For an aurora observer, it makes most sense to give names to the basic auroral forms. Below are descriptions of some of the best known ones.

The simplest form taken by an aurora is a *glow* on the horizon. This is the type of aurora most frequently seen from low latitudes. Because of its low level of brightness, the colour may be difficult to discern and it often appears as a pale green or greyish glow in the northern horizon and is most easily noticed from very dark areas. It is therefore very important to get away from cities, with their street lights and other artificial lights, and allow your eyes to adapt to the dark. Such a glow is also more easily seen on nights without moonlight. If you are not sure what you're looking at, try to see if stars are visible through the glow or take a photo: if the glow appears green in colour and if you can see stars through it, then you are looking at aurora glow.

The most typical form of aurora seen from high, mid and low altitudes is an *arc*, which looks like a green bow stretching from east to west with uniform brightness. This typically green light is emitted by oxygen atoms as they collide with high-energy electrons. When aurora activity is high, arcs may also be seen from low latitudes and sometimes vertical structures, too, can be made out.

Typically, an arc may develop into a *band*, which is the type of aurora that perhaps most people first think of when they hear the term "northern lights". A band differs from an arc in that it has a ribbon-like structure and usually exhibits folds and snake-like shapes that span across the sky. There may also be several parallel bands.

When the aurora becomes more active, a band tends to develop vertical *rays* which are aligned along the direction of the Earth's magnetic field. When the rays, which appear as brighter vertical bundles, move horizontally along an arc or a band, the bands start to look like *curtains* or *draperies* that seem to blow in a breeze across the sky. This is the type of aurora that is often reproduced in paintings and drawings, such as the famous woodcut by the Norwegian polar explorer and humanitarian Fridtjof Nansen. As the activity increases even more, the bottom of the folded curtain is often the brightest part, and during energetic displays the

PREVIOUS PAGE
Because the eastern and western ends of an aurora band is located further away from an observer than the head-on view an aurora looks like an arch over the northern horizon. During mild auroral activity this is the most commonly seen type of aurora.

RIGHT
The perspective makes an aurora band or curtain look different for an aurora watcher located south of the aurora oval compared to an observer who is located directly underneath the aurora.

For an observer located south of the aurora oval, a band with vertical rays, or a curtain, typically stretches from east to west in an arc. The far ends of the bands look thinner because of the greater distance from the observer (as seen in the two mirror-images). The head-on view reveals a band or a curtain with vertical rays (upper left). For an observer located directly underneath the same curtain the view would look entirely different and the observer would see a corona (bottom left). While the curtain and the corona look like two completely different structures they are in fact the same thing, but the perspective causes the rays to seem to converge near the zenith. Note the purple-pinkish light in the lower part of the corona which is caused by excited nitrogen molecules, whereas the upper part is dominated by green.

lower part is often tinted with a very distinct purple-pinkish light that is emitted by excited nitrogen molecules, whereas the upper part is dominated by green. During strong auroras, a blood-red colour may be seen in the upper part of an otherwise green curtain. Completely all-red auroras may also sometimes be seen, a consequence of oxygen atoms being struck by low-energy electrons.

One of the most spectacular sights that can be observed during an aurora display is a *corona* or a *northern lights crown*. Although a corona is not itself a distinctive type of aurora, it certainly looks like nothing else. A corona can only be seen when the aurora is located directly above one's head and the perspective causes the rays in the bands or curtains to appear to converge near the zenith and to stretch out in all directions. Viewed by an observer further south, the same corona will be seen as a rayed band or curtain. The movement of the aurora is very fast during a corona, and the most spectacular colours and patterns may be observed. When it is directly above you, in the magnetic zenith, it is also possible to get an idea of how very thin an auroral arc or band really is. While its height may be tens or hundreds of kilometres and its length several thousand kilometres, the width is in fact often no more than 100 meters. When seen only a short distance from the magnetic zenith, however, it appears as a broad structure where the middle band located directly above the observer is extremely thin, while similar bands seen at a slight angle are perceived as broad curtains.

Other recognisable forms include *patches*, which don't have clearly defined shapes or edges, and *veils*, which may be described as a homogeneous background glow with a low level of brightness.

In addition to the above-mentioned forms, auroras may also be characterized by their intensity and condition – for example, according to how fast their activity is, their changes in brightness, and their colour.

At times of increased auroral activity, many of the above-mentioned structures may often be observable during a single night. A display will typically begin as an arc in the far north that will develop into bands and curtains featuring more distinct structural elements, such as vertical rays. This is the expansive phase. As the activity increases, rapid movement and the build-up of several bands may follow and the auroras will usually be seen higher up in the sky, where they may form the most amazing structures. During this phase, an increase in brightness usually occurs, and if you are lucky and situated directly under the auroras, a corona may form in all its magnificence above your head. As the activity starts to subside, the forms will become more and more diffuse and fade. After some time, often one to two hours, activity may increase again. Sometimes it will be possible to observe several such cycles in the course of a single night. In the early morning hours after

LEFT
In early fall or late spring, a rare purple type of auroras can sometimes be seen just before sunrise when the sunlight is falling on ionized nitrogen molecules in the high atmosphere. This may cause an intensified emission of light. The photo, which also shows the full moon, is taken in the early morning hours in the beginning of October.

NEXT PAGE
Aurora curtain with vertical rays.

a strong outburst, the sky will often be filled with a green mist, and another, but less familiar, kind of aurora may be seen – a *pulsating aurora*.

Few people have heard of pulsating auroras, even though they are, in fact, one of the most common types of auroras. The reason for this is that they are diffuse and weak. They are also mostly seen in the early morning hours after the «normal» display is over. Unlike the bright or discrete auroras, pulsating auroras do not sweep over the sky. Instead they often take the form of several patches of dull green haze in the sky that seem to blink on and off or pulsate – hence the name. The patches are often large and seem to have lives of their own, independent of one another. The patches are short-lived, typically lasting for a period of between a few seconds and ten or fifteen seconds. Watching pulsating auroras can be very fascinating, but usually requires a dark sky.

RIGHT
The Milky Way and faint auroras as seen from a dark area. The Andromeda Galaxy can be glimpsed as a diffuse oval-shaped structure in the upper right of the photo.

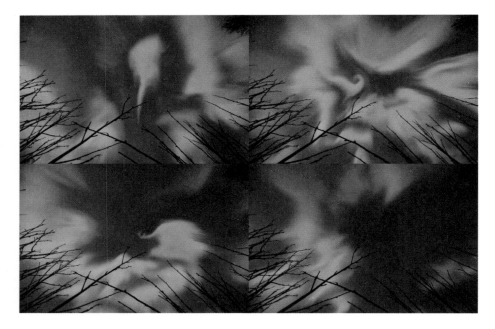

Photographs of pulsating patches taken at intervals of 10 seconds.

PRACTICAL OBSERVATION OF THE NORTHERN LIGHTS

Finding a dark area

No optical aids such as binoculars are needed to observe auroras; the best way to see them is simply with your eyes. What you need to increase your chances of seeing them, however, is a dark area away from urban areas and other sources of light pollution. Finding a dark spot from which to observe them has become increasingly difficult, and even far away from cities it can be quite astonishing to notice the extent to which people light up their homes and their surroundings from dusk to dawn. The view of the night sky that almost all of us had only 50 years ago is now largely gone, and in many areas it is no longer possible to see more than a handful of the brightest stars, let alone fainter structures such as the Milky Way and auroras. Ask the local association of amateur astronomers for advice on finding a dark observation spot: they will be very familiar with the problem and will probably have many good suggestions.

How to dress for observing auroras

Having found a dark place, all you need is some patience and good clothing to keep you warm in the cold winter night. Whether you are observing from relatively mild low latitudes, such as in central Europe, or if you are in an area in the far north near the Arctic Circle, it is important to dress properly for the weather and to be prepared to wait some time before the auroras materialize. You may, of course, wait inside a house or in a car, but in that case remember to look out often. Very often. In the course of just a few minutes, a sky with no trace of auroras whatsoever can change to one covered in green bands. Although waiting outside on a beautiful winter night with the entire sky sparkling with stars above your head is far from boring, being comfortable and warm will greatly increase your enjoyment of the experience.

The usual recommendation for clothing in cold temperatures, the so-called layer principle, also applies for aurora observers, but slightly less so than if you are more active and need an outlet for your body heat. The most important thing is the closest layer to your skin. By far the best material to wear is wool or, perhaps, synthetic polypropylene. Never wear cotton; perspiration has nowhere to go if you have cotton against your skin and it will cling to your body and make you cold. Unlike cotton, wool will still keep you warm even if it gets moist; it is recommended that you wear wool both on your upper body and on your feet. Anyone who has spent a long time outside in the cold knows that if you don't move much your feet will become cold fairly quickly, even if you are well dressed. Good winter boots that allow extra space for

PREVIOUS PAGE
Northern lights can easily be seen also
when the full moon is up.

socks and air are definitely worth the price when you are out in the cold. For safety, a sleeping bag or a survival foil heat blanket is always worth having. A good jacket and insulated trousers, or, even better, a thermo-suit can make the difference between an uncomfortably cold experience and pleasant viewing. Remember to always wear proper gloves and headwear. A balaclava with a wind stopper is a wonderful thing to have, but usually a good woollen hat will suffice, in combination with the hood on your jacket. Remember that it doesn't matter how you look out there in the night – functionality and comfort matter far more than appearance. After you catch your first glimpse of auroras flickering across the sky, all thoughts about being cold will usually vanish, and no matter how many times you have seen the auroras, it will come naturally to jump up and down like a happy child.

Other useful equipment

In addition to clothing, you will want to bring some food and a thermos bottle containing something warm to drink. Basic emergency equipment and a good headlamp or torch are also highly recommended. It can be difficult to see in the dark, and there may be very slippery ice; you don't want to start or end your night under the auroras with a broken leg or a ruined camera. As with any kind of night-time observation, you will be able to see auroras much more easily if your eyes are adapted to the dark. It takes approximately 20 to 30 minutes for eyes to fully adapt from bright light to complete darkness. Here is a tip to avoid ruining your night vision: if you are using a headlamp to see where you are walking or as an aid while setting up your equipment, make it a red headlamp. This will preserve both your own night vision and that of your fellow observers.

What to expect?

An extremely reasonable question that is asked by many people who have never seen auroras with their own eyes is how bright they actually are, how well the different colours can be seen compared to photos, and how fast the auroras actually move. The answers to all these questions will depend on the intensity of the auroras, but during an active display you can very easily see the green and the purple hues. The red can be somewhat more difficult to see, but may sometimes even dominate and appear to the eye as a deep blood-red. While it is definitely possible to see rather strong colours with the eyes, a camera can gather light for a longer time, so that the colours will often appear more intense in a photo than in real life.

As for brightness, very bright auroras can easily light up the surface of a lake, the sea, or a snow-clad landscape so that the ground or water surface actually looks green; but normally they are much fainter. At high latitudes, auroras may be seen during a full moon without any difficulty and the photo below gives a fairly accurate impression of what one such aurora may look like.

One of the most commonly asked questions is whether, and how rapidly, auroras actually move. This depends a great deal on the activity. Arcs and bands may be more or less stationary, whereas more active bands and curtains can move and change shape very quickly indeed. Most, but not all, videos of auroras are sped up to various degrees and the movement seen in many videos or time-lapse movies is often exaggerated, but during the most intensive phase of a display, bands can travel across the entire sky very rapidly indeed, and the movement experienced when the rayed curtains form a corona above one's head can be almost unbelievable.

CHAPTER FIVE

Photographing
the Northern Lights

The beauty of the northern lights has been described by many people in a variety of ways. Innumerable explorers, musicians, artists, photographers, and poets who have been inspired by their beauty have tried to put words to what they have seen. Perhaps no one has come closer to an accurate description of them than the Austro-Hungarian Arctic explorer Julius von Payer (1841-1915), who once wrote that "No pencil can draw it, no colours can paint it, and no words can describe it in all its magnificence". Undoubtedly, the feeling of standing enchanted under the auroras on a clear winter night when the rays and curtains flicker and shimmer above one's head simply cannot be reproduced – it has to be experienced.

Even though full justice cannot be done to their magnificence, many of us naturally wish to capture the auroras not only with our eyes but also with a camera, and in fact photographs of auroras can come pretty close to the real thing. Aurora photography can be tremendously rewarding, and some of the most majestic photos taken on our planet are photos of auroras.

Aurora photography is not difficult. Very satisfactory results, which will continue to bring pleasure throughout one's lifetime, can be obtained by rather simple means. For the best results, however, some general guidelines need to be followed, and, as with all photography, the quality of the picture will depend on the experience of the photographer. In this chapter, we will briefly describe how best to go about photographing auroras.

CHOICE OF CAMERA

Auroras can be recorded with most cameras, ranging from simple "point-and-shoot" cameras to more or less advanced single lens reflex (SLR) cameras. The best type of camera for photographing the northern lights is a Digital Single Lens Reflex camera (or DSLR for short), and the main focus of this chapter will be on the use of DSLRs, but, as described below, it is also possible to use other types of cameras successfully following the same general guidelines.

Digital compact cameras

Many of us own a small compact camera that we use for ordinary everyday photography. Can such a camera also be used to take photos of auroras at night? There are, of course, major differences among the various brands and models, but when a camera is mounted on a tripod, it is usually possible to photograph at least bright auroras with satisfactory results. Some compact cameras are better suited than others to nighttime photography, however, and in general the higher degree of manual control your camera permits, the better. Since compact cameras are designed for daytime use and are usually equipped with small sensors and lenses with narrow small openings, they do not allow enough light to reach the sensor to capture anything but the brightest auroras. However, most models have at least one type of setting that allow for longer exposures, often called "fireworks" or "night" and if you have this setting on your camera, use it. It is not optimal, but

With the right settings, good aurora photos can be obtained with a simple digital compact camera.

it is definitely worth trying and may result in very nice photos. Remember to turn off the flash and the autofocus, to use a tripod and to use the camera's self-timer to avoid vibration. Make sure you learn how to operate your camera in night-mode in advance so that you don't have to try to find this out in the dark. Many "hybrid" digital cameras carry larger sensors and also offer the option to switch lenses and thus offer some of the advantages and flexibility DSLRs, and may therefore be better suited for the job.

Digital single reflex cameras (DSLR)

Almost all DSLRs are very well suited for photographing auroras. The huge advantage of a DSLR compared to a compact camera is that it provides the photographer with full manual control over the settings and has interchangeable lenses. If you already own a DSLR, the good news is that no matter what brand or model you have, it will most likely be up to the job even if there are considerable differences among various DSLRs. If you are about to buy a DSLR, you are probably not going to choose your model based upon its suitability for nocturnal photography (unless you are a dedicated astro-photographer), but will probably go instead for a camera that suits your normal daytime photography needs (as well as your budget). The market contains many good models at a wide variety of prices, ranging from entry-level cameras to high-end products for professional use, but all of them offer full manual control and are therefore well suited to the purpose at hand. If you are

DSLR cameras are particularly well suited for aurora photography since they offer the photographer full manual control over the settings and interchangeable lenses.

looking for a DSLR that is particularly well suited for nighttime photography, you will want to look into the high-end models with large CMOS sensors and good low-noise performance. More important than what type or model you have is how you use it and what kind of lens you attach to it. The following sections offer advice on what kind of lenses that gives good results and which settings to use in different situations as well as some suggestions about helpful accessories.

Video cameras

It is possible to record auroras with a video camera or by using the video function available on many digital cameras, but the result is often very poor. Fairly satisfactory results can be obtained with advanced and supersensitive video cameras, as well as with the video function on high-end DSLRs at high ISO settings, but for the normal photographer, this is usually not an option. If you wish to create high-quality videos of auroras, the best approach is to create a time-lapse video. Giving detailed instructions on this procedure is beyond the scope of this book, but the technique is fairly straightforward and involves using a DSLR to take a sequence of images of the sky with a time interval between successive images. To turn the images into a video, you will need a computer with software that will edit the images and combine them to form a movie.

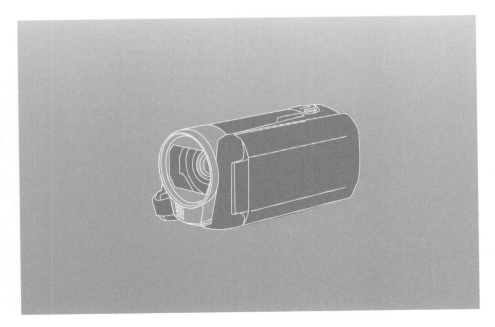

Most video cameras are not able to record auroras in a satisfactory way. For making high quality videos of auroras time-lapse photography with a DSLR is usually the preferred technique.

CHOICE OF LENS

The northern lights usually extend across a large portion of the sky. If you wish to record as much of the view as possible, a wide-angle lens somewhere in the range of 8 to 50 mm is preferable. A focal length of around 20 mm is usually a good starting point, but remember that a lens with a given focal length will cover different angles of views, depending on the size of your camera's image sensor. For the best results, you will need a so-called fast lens. Lens speed has nothing to do with the autofocus speed of the lens, but is simply a description of how much light the lens transmits, which is expressed as an f-number (or an f-stop). The smaller the f-number, the more light can be captured during a certain period, meaning that the shutter speed can be kept quicker – thus the term "fast" lens. Without a fast lens, you will need to use longer exposures or higher ISO settings, which will blur the structure of the aurora or increase the image noise. Normally a lens is considered "fast" if the f-number is 2.8 or lower. The downside of fast lenses is that they are usually more expensive than slower lenses, but they are well worth the money if you are serious about aurora photography. If a fast wide-angle lens is beyond your budget, you might want to check out the second-hand market. Since the digital revolution, it has been possible to purchase many manual, non-AF lenses at fairly low prices, and they usually work very well when one is photographing auroras. Remember to check that the lens fits your camera body. Most lenses perform best when not fully open. Another advantage of having a fast lens is that you can go

For the best results, a fast wide-angle lens should be used.

down one or two steps and thereby often capture sharper images while still taking in enough light to record the auroras. Unless the auroras are very bright, it is usually best to shoot with the lens "wide open" (that is, at the lowest f-number).

BASIC SETTINGS FOR AURORA PHOTOGRAPHY

While it is fairly easy to photograph auroras with a DSLR, it is difficult to give general technical advice that will apply to all users. We all have different equipment and different ideas as to how we wish to capture the auroras. The intensity and brightness of auroras may also vary considerably and can change rapidly in a short time, and it might therefore be necessary to change camera settings several times during a single aurora display. If you are taking pictures of an aurora under a dark moonless sky, it naturally requires different settings than if you are shooting on a snow-clad landscape under a full moon. Once you have learned the general guidelines, however, you will easily be able to adjust the settings depending on the situation.

Set you camera in Manual Mode to take control over the camera's settings.

Shooting mode

Use manual mode. If you are experienced and have a really fast lens, you can shoot bright auroras in aperture-priority mode, but for almost all situations manual mode is recommended.

Shutter speed

A good starting point for medium-bright auroras is to set the exposure time at somewhere between 5 and 20 seconds and then adjust it based upon the aurora's appearance. Auroras often have many interesting structures, and for really fast-moving and bright auroras, you need to go down dramatically in exposure time (1-2 seconds) in order to be able to capture finer details, such as vertical rays or the structures in a corona. For less bright auroras, such as a glow or an arc low on the northern horizon, a long exposure is usually preferable. At lower latitudes, it might be a good idea to keep the exposures at around 30 seconds or more on dark nights. At longer exposures than that, the stars begin to appear as trails. This problem is less noticeable if you use a wide-angle lens as opposed to a lens with greater magnification. To avoid this problem, you can set the ISO value higher while keeping the exposure at around 30 seconds. Or else you can simply accept the star trails in the photo. You can also use the effect of a long exposure to your advantage and take star-trail photos. This can be very rewarding and will often result in interesting photos. It is also possible to compensate for the Earth's rotation by mounting the camera on a tracking platform but this is often beyond the scope of most aurora photographers.

A good starting point for aurora photography is to use exposures between 5 and 20 seconds depending on the brightness of the auroras.

If you are photographing from a moving ship you will be forced to keep exposures as short as possible to avoid getting blurry photos. Exposures of around 2-5 seconds at ISO values as high as 1000-2000 are recommended. Even so, some blurring of your pictures must be expected, even if you lean the camera against something on the boat.

Aperture

For most aurora photography, it is recommended that you use the widest aperture you can (that is, the one with the lowest f-number), which is usually f/1.8, f/2.8 or f/3.5, depending on the speed of your lens.

ISO setting

ISO can be described as a measure of the sensitivity to light of the image sensor. The lower the ISO number, the less sensitive your camera is to light. High ISO settings are therefore often used in darker situations to enable the photographer to use faster shutter speeds (shorter exposures). Relatively high ISO settings (400 – 1600) are therefore commonly used in aurora photography. The cost of using a high ISO setting is that you get noisier shots, especially in the dark areas of the image. Some of the noise can be fixed in post-processing (see also "Noise reduction" below). Today, most people use digital cameras on which the ISO settings can be adjusted and changed easily from one exposure to the next, making it easy to see immediately the ways in which various settings affect the image.

To be able to capture finer details and structures in the auroras a comparably high ISO-setting is preferable. An ISO-value of 800 is a good starting point.

File format

If your camera permits it, it is recommended that you shoot your images in both RAW and JPEG, or only in RAW. Even if you are not familiar with working or processing RAW files, there almost always comes a stage at which every photographer starts to realise the advantages of shooting in RAW. If you are not there yet, shoot in both formats and work with JPEGs for the time being and simply store the RAW files until you feel ready to explore the possibilities. RAW is not an image file format as such, but should rather be considered as a negative, that is, as something that is not immediately usable as an image but that contains all the information needed to create one. RAW files contain a lot more information and therefore have a much higher tolerance to processing than JPEGs. JPEGs can, of course, also be edited, but the disadvantage is that a lot of the information stored in a JPG is thereby lost forever, whereas RAW files can be used to bring out details – in, for example, the highlight and shadow areas – that might be particularly important for aurora photos taken under difficult light conditions.

Record your images in RAW (or both RAW and JPEG).

White balance

The white balance setting you choose is not very critical, especially not if you shoot RAW files. If in doubt, however, set your white balance at "Daylight". If you are shooting in areas dominated by street lamps, the "Fluorescent" setting can be used with good results.

Noise reduction

When using high ISO settings, you will end up with more noise or "grain" in the photos. In compact cameras, this unwanted effect is often noticeable already at ISO values as low as 400, while in most DSLRs settings as high as ISO 1000 to 1600 can usually be used without noise becoming too much of an issue. As indicated above, high ISO settings are often necessary if one wishes to capture finer details in auroras, and noise will therefore often be more of a problem for the aurora photographer than for the photographer of normal daytime subjects. The best time to deal with noise is during RAW conversion and/or post-processing. Many DSLRs also have settings, often hidden deep in the drop-down menus, which can control noise – for example "High ISO Noise Reduction" and "Long Exposure Noise Reduction". You may want to experiment with these settings, but in general the best advice is to handle noise in post-processing, and unless you know how your camera's settings affect the different types of noise, don't bother with them. Long Exposure Noise Reduction may be worthwhile to use if your camera is giving you a lot of trouble with hot pixels, but keep in mind that, when this setting is used, the camera, after it has finished taking the photo, will immediately start to record a so-called "dark frame". It takes some time for the camera to do this (a time equal to the exposure time of your shot), and you will usually not want to wait for this process to be completed in the middle of a spectacular aurora display. In most cases, then, it is recommended that you turn this setting off.

Focusing

It is easy to focus during the daytime, whether by using autofocus or by looking through the viewfinder. At night, however, it can be a bit more of a challenge. Normally you will want to have your focus on infinity, but many lenses focus past infinity, and putting the lens focus ring at infinity is therefore not a guarantee that you will get the correct focus. If your camera has a live view (LV) function, use it. Aim at a bright star, the moon, or a distant streetlamp to obtain the correct focus. If your camera doesn't have live view, a good way to get the proper focus is to temporarily switch on autofocus (AF), point the camera towards a distant bright object, focus, and then switch back to manual. To ensure that the focus stays the way you want it, it is a good idea to tape the focus ring so that it doesn't accidentally slip out of

The camera's white balance modes only affect jpegs. It is recommended to shoot in RAW and deal with white balance in post-processing. If you shoot in JPEG only, the daylight setting is usually a good choice.

Noise can be a problem when photographing auroras. This is best dealt with during image post-processing. The photo shows a close-up section of a particularly noisy image taken at a high ISO-setting. While it is not possible to completely get rid of image noise in already noisy shots, noise reduction can help.

focus. Make sure that you use a tape that doesn't damage the focus ring or the barrel of the lens.

Composition

How you compose your images, of course, depends entirely on your own taste. Many beginners tend to focus too much on the auroras and forget about the composition. In the dark, moreover, it can be difficult to determine whether unwanted objects, such as telephone wires, are in your way. Including an interesting foreground object, such as a tree or a person, makes your aurora photos more interesting. Since auroras often take up a large part of the sky, including a house or a person in a picture can help the viewer to realise the scale of the phenomenon.

Just as with normal daytime photography an interesting composition can make a big difference to a photo. Try to include a foreground or a person or use the different shapes of the auroras to compose interesting photos. Even a very faint arc in the horizon can look very impressive if it is reflected in a water surface.

USEFUL ACCESSORIES

Tripod

For aurora photography, it is absolutely necessary to use a tripod, since your exposure times will exceed several seconds. A sturdy, and preferably high, tripod with a heavy-duty ball head is recommended for its versatility. A ball head makes it very quick and easy to switch between horizontal and vertical shots, something you are likely to do several times during an aurora display. If you don't have a tripod handy, or if you are photographing from a moving boat or from an airplane, try to keep the exposure time down by going up in ISO value and try to stabilize the camera on something. If you are travelling and don't want to transport a bulky tripod, consider renting or borrowing one (many tour operators offer this option), but remember that the tripod is as important as the camera for aurora photography. Also remember to place the tripod on firm ground and make sure the camera is tight.

Filter

Never use a filter on your lens when photographing auroras. Even if you only have a "harmless" UV-filter or the like to protect the lens, remove it. Depending on the type of filter you have, it will either leave you with unwanted concentric rings on the photo (also known as Newton's rings) or reduce the light and thus, in a way, make your lens slower.

Cable release / self-timer

To reduce camera vibration, use a shutter-release cable or an infrared remote control. If you don't have one, you can also use the self-timer of your camera. It can also be a good idea to use the exposure delay mode, if your camera has it.

Batteries

Make sure your battery is fully loaded before you go out photographing. Few things sap the energy of batteries more than long exposures in cold temperatures. Bring one or two fully charged extra batteries with you if you have them. Carry them close to your body so that they will stay relatively warm. Remember to check the battery level at regular intervals and replace it with a fresh one before it is completely depleted.

The picture shows a typical photo setup for aurora photography. A DSLR camera with a wide-angle lens has been mounted on a heavy tripod with a ball-head. A cable release is attached to the camera and the focus ring has been taped to keep focus correct throughout the night.

Always bring one or two fully charged extra batteries with you when you go out.

Memory card

The type and storage capacity of the memory card you will need depends on the file format you shoot in and the number of photos you plan to shoot, but it is recommended that you use a relatively high-capacity memory card with plenty of space. An empty back-up card is always handy. If you are out on a journey, you can never have too much memory. For time-lapse photography, it is essential that you have several high-speed memory cards with large storage capacity.

Headlamp

When you are out there in the dark, you are likely to find yourself walking around in slippery and dark places while carrying your equipment. A headlamp is therefore highly recommended. With a headlamp, both your hands are free and you can easily make adjustments to your camera. Be sure to turn off your headlamp before taking your photo. Remember that it takes about 20 to 30 minutes to regain most of your night vision after being exposed to bright light. To preserve your, and others', night vision, a low-intensity red headlamp or flash lamp is recommended. With such a lamp, you can make necessary adjustments and be able to appreciate the night sky and the auroras without having to wait another half an hour for your night vision to return.

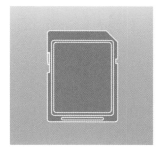

An extra memory card with plenty of space is always a good thing to bring with you, especially if you plan to shoot aurora time-lapse photography.

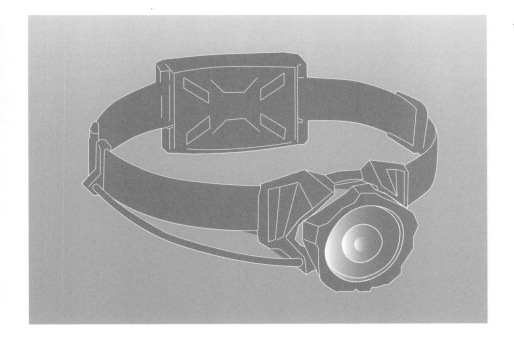

A headlamp comes highly recommended when you walk around with your equipment in the dark and leaves both your hands free to make adjustments to your camera.

NIGHT-TIME AND COLD-WEATHER PHOTOGRAPHY

Often, the key to a good aurora photo is preparation. Many stunning aurora photos are simply the result of the photographer being in the right place at the right time, with the equipment ready and tested. When the auroras begin dancing across the sky, it is very common to discover that one's camera isn't ready for night photography, that it is hard to find a good spot in the dark, and that there just isn't enough time to get all the settings right. Learning how to operate the camera during the daytime and taking precautions for photographing in cold conditions will prevent a good many frustrations in the field.

Start looking for good places in daylight that you might want to return to, and remember to pick a place where light pollution is at a minimum. When aurora forecasts are looking good, it pays to get out and be ready before the auroras are in full swing. Experienced aurora photographers know that they might have to wait for a long time before the show begins, but when it does they don't need to set things up in a hurry and can try out different settings and compositions beforehand.

One of the most familiar and frustrating parts of photographing in the cold is that you will sooner or later discover that dew or ice has formed on your lens. Dew on the equipment can completely ruin a photo session and is the bane of many nocturnal photographers. While it is difficult to completely ensure yourself against dew formation, you can go a long way toward preventing it by letting your

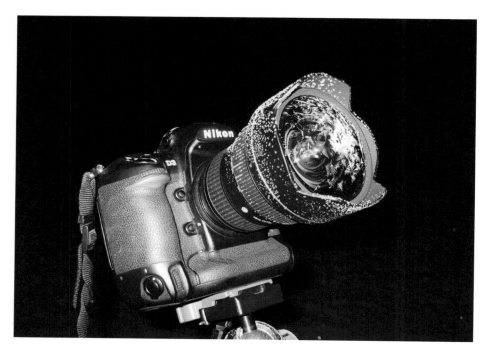

equipment adjust to the outside temperature before you start shooting. In the evening before you go out, remove the battery from the camera and then put the camera in a plastic bag and place it outside, in a safe place, in the temperature in which you plan to shoot. The best approach is to use a normal plastic waste bag with the air squeezed out. This might seem like an unnecessary and time-consuming precaution, but by taking this simple step you will save a lot of time and frustration in the field.

When out photographing, avoid taking the camera in and out of your car or house and avoid holding your hands on the lens and try not to breathe on the lens and camera. Check the lens for dew by using a headlamp at regular intervals, especially if you are handling the camera a lot.

When you bring your equipment into a warm interior from a shooting session in the cold outdoors, dew will form instantly. To avoid this, put your equipment in a plastic bag and wait for it to adjust to the indoor temperature. Dew will then form on the outside and your equipment will stay dry and you are less likely to damage the equipment.

As you become more experienced and find yourself bitten by the night-photo bug, you will find that most, if not all, of the steps involved in aurora photography will become second nature to you, and that the world at night is just as fascinating to capture with a camera as the world by day.

Concluding remarks

Observing and photographing auroras is something of a holy grail and many people dream of seeing this natural wonder with their own eyes once in life. By combining our experiences from living and working with auroras in the land of the northern lights we hope that this guide will be a helpful companion and offer guidance to maximise your chances of experiencing the magic of the auroras for a long time to come. The deep fascination of the northern lights has profoundly changed the life of both authors of this book and having seen countless aurora displays from many different places on Earth we are both keen aurora watchers. It is possible to observe, enjoy and photograph the northern lights from many different places on Earth. Whether you live in the high north where the northern lights are a common sight, or further south, where strong aurora displays are less common, we wish you all clear skies and best of luck in your search for the northern lights. By keeping an eye on space weather forecasts, just like you keep your eyes on the normal weather forecasts, you may very well be rewarded with a sight that you will never forget.

OPPOSITE PAGE
By using long exposures it is possible to take interesting star-trail photos. Combined with auroras and an interesting composition this technique can give very rewarding results. The exposure time in the photo to the left was 60 minutes at ISO 200.

NEXT PAGE
One of the modern-day challenges of night-time photography is how to deal with light pollution. Try to find a dark area away from city lights for your aurora- and star-watching. Even a short distance out of town is better than the middle of a city where most or all stars are washed out.